This book belongs to:

_____

_____

_____

"I only appear when I really need to.
So please if you see me, listen, won't you?"

The Enough Sayer

On being honest

This is Tilly.
Tilly has no pets.
But at school today,
This is not what she said...

She made up lies to impress her friends.
She was lying and lying, over again.

"I have a cat and a dog, and a really green frog,
and..."

But before she could finish
The Enough Sayer appeared!

"ENOUGH, ENOUGH!"
"No more lies, do you hear!"

Tilly continued...
"I have a cute little mouse,
a giraffe,
and a hippo that live in my house!"

...The Enough Sayer shouted,
But Tilly couldn't stop, she was too *excited*.

One final attempt to stop her lies,
The Enough Sayer said loudly, into the sky....

"When I say ENOUGH don't HUFF and don't PUFF
Listen to what I say or you'll regret it one day"

Shrugging her shoulders, Tilly did not care.
She went on to talk about her big grizzly bear.

Very unimpressed, The Enough Sayer left.

When Tilly got home she was very surprised. She saw all of her friends standing outside.

Starting to panic, Tilly thought to herself:

I made all of this up,
What do I do now?

If I let them in,
They'll know I was lying...

And in front of them all, Tilly started crying

"Oh why did I lie about all of this stuff?
Why didn't I listen when I was told, enough?
I'm so sorry my friends, I am so upset,
I lied to you all about my house full of pets"

"You were all so impressed
And it made me feel cool,
But the truth is... Well...
I have no pets at all."

She never thought lying would make her feel so bad,
Until she realised her actions made others feel sad.

Then what came next was never expected.
They all started smiling,
It was the truth they respected.

"Listen Tilly, you never had to pretend
You've never had pets,
And yet we've always been friends.

We love you Tilly, when you're being yourself,
We'd never want you to be someone else.

So please be honest,
Because that's what friends do
You're here for us and we're here for you"

Tilly had never been so happy,
With her friends by her side,
Then she spotted The Enough Sayer
From the corner of her eye.

She made her way over
And sheepishly said:

"I know if I listened,
I could have avoided this mess"

The Enough Sayer smiled
And waved Tilly goodbye.

Now knowing she'd never,
Again, tell a lie.

Made in the USA
Coppell, TX
29 October 2021